THIS BOOK BELONGS TO

This book is dedicated to all the parents who are helping their children "grow grateful." Together, we're working to grow a generation of adults that recognize all the beauty and goodness around them, even in difficult times. This gift will lead to deeper learning, connection, understanding, compassion, and happiness. Really, what more could we want for our children?

And for my daughters, always for my daughters. Everything I do is for you, my loves.

Printed in the United States of America
First Printing, 2019
Four Little Birds Publishing

vickeryandco.com

ISBN 978-1-7336185-1-9

Cover design *by* Tiffanie Tran
Layout & typesetting *by* Jessie Leiber
Copyediting *by* Erin Giberson

All quotes are with permission of the original author and their parents, if necessary.

Introduction

"Gratitude feels like something happy inside you that would result in a smile or tears of joy or yelling thank you so much. It feels warm when you have gratitude, not like it's hot outside but it's a happy warm."

SIMRYN, AGE 9

Gratitude for the Whole Family

Last year I published my first book, *Gratitude Journal: Shift Your Focus*. This book was designed to help adults develop powerful gratitude practices that elevate and enrich their lives, personally and professionally.

Almost as soon as the book hit the shelves, I began receiving requests to produce one specifically for kids and families. Developing gratitude rituals proved impactful for the adults who used the book, and it was instantly obvious that this was an easy, approachable way to teach children about the importance of acknowledging and expressing gratitude.

I've made a few changes to this version of the book to offer more opportunities for parents and children to discuss gratitude, personal wins, and *why* these things are important not only to acknowledge — but also to truly understand and share!

I had a bit of an epiphany after asking parents to talk with their kids about gratitude. I wanted to use quotes in the book (I love quotes!) and felt it appropriate to quote children in this version as I quoted thought leaders in the original book. One of the parents I spoke with is a good friend. Her daughter Ryann is a very close friend of my daughter, Tessa, and was an exuberant participant in this conversation. She truly is one of the sweetest, most inviting young people I know, and she was very forthcoming when talking about gratitude. But what I found interesting was her distinction between "Gratitude" and "Gratefulness."

Ryann said she believes gratitude and being grateful are different things. She said, "I can be grateful for something and feel that inside, but gratitude is actually expressing that gratefulness [to others]!" Well, of course, she's completely correct! Gratitude is internal, and gratefulness is external. They are different emotions, and we express and feel them differently. Moreover, there's a difference between expressing gratitude outwardly to ourselves (like we do in this book) and *sharing* our gratitude with others when we feel grateful.

Thanks to Ryann, I've added two new prompts in this journal: "What went well today, and why?" and "How did you express your gratitude today?" When we stop and think about what behaviors and actions lead to "good things happening," we're able to begin intentionally building healthy habits that lead to more good things happening! And, it's just as important to reflect on how gratefulness towards others impacts everyone. This is just as important as expressing gratitude internally.

The other interesting thing I noticed through these conversations is that teenagers were actually *less* able to go deeper than "gratitude is being thankful" than the younger kids. Now, I don't think this is because teenagers lack gratitude or feelings of thanks. What I do think, however, is that without a foundation of understanding why a gratitude practice is helpful and how it can improve your life, we don't slow down long enough to appreciate these gifts, and they tend to pass us by unnoticed. In short, learning to experience your life's blessings, in the moment, and day after day, is a learned skill. And, once learned, this becomes a powerful tool in creating well-being and living a more joyful life.

Finally, it's my hope that by using this journal, children (and adults alike) will learn to be grateful for *themselves*. To recognize their own bravery, kindness, strength, and self-love. This gratitude practice helps develop emotional openness and recognition by allowing us to see ourselves, our actions, and different possibilities in a new and beautiful light.

A Note About the Title of This Book

Naming a book isn't much different than naming a child. That may sound ridiculous, but that's been my experience twice now. I went through a number of different titles for this book before landing on "Grow Grateful." I chose this title because I wanted a name that encompassed taking action, creating change, and ... well, growing. For me, practicing gratitude is an ever-evolving process, and it creates the opportunity to grow. Every single day, when I sit down to list out my gratitude, I learn something new about myself. I explore parts of my heart and my life that had been previously untapped or unrecognized.

Practicing gratitude helps us see the inevitable intersections of life, which is what I recognize as the messy, wonderful dynamic of being alive with all the experiences and emotions that it entails. Life, in all its glory, is multilayered. It's why we're able to be both happy and sad at the same time, and it's why we can find things to be grateful for during difficult or painful moments. It often starts with simply accepting the range of feelings we have throughout each day and exploring what causes those emotions.

As an example, a moment of intersectional gratitude may occur after I've given a keynote speech and find myself processing the evening, in that I can feel grateful to an audience member who said my speech really connected with her. I can also express gratitude for the opportunity to share my story with the crowd and for the money earned. I may even go so far as to say I'm grateful for the ability to take my kids on a special outing because of the income from giving the speech. I could easily just say, "I'm grateful for being asked to speak," which is true, but it's deeper than that and a whole lot more nuanced. These moments are all connected and intertwined. In this way, they elicit different feelings of gratitude that uniquely and poignantly connect with my life.

When I practice gratitude, whether on my own or with my children, I constantly learn more about myself, how I move through the world, what I have to offer, what I want to learn, and who I want to be. When it came to naming this book, I wanted the title to convey to you, the reader, that by purchasing this item, you'll experience growth and be able to share what this creates in your life with your loved ones. You'll learn so much about yourself and, most importantly, you'll nurture your own ability to grow.

Thank you to the many people who talked me through this naming process. I'm grateful for your insight, your willingness to listen and push me, and, eventually, your understanding and acceptance of my final decision, even if it wasn't your favorite choice.

To you, dear readers and journalers, may every moment of this experience help you Grow Grateful.

Just Because It's Worth It, Doesn't Mean It's Easy

"When you express gratitude, people around you can tell if you actually mean it!"

- **Jason, age 14**

When I was preparing to write this book I engaged all four of my daughters (ages 6-15) in conversation about gratitude. It was the same conversation I had with parents and children all over the world as I prepped for this book.

I asked each of them, one on one: "Hi, sweetie, I'd love to know what gratitude means to you. How do you feel when you're grateful? How do you express gratitude?" And all four times I was met with a blank stare, shrugged shoulders and "I don't know." What, I thought? Wait a minute ... we share gratitude every single night at the dinner table, and I yell out what I'm grateful for a million times a day. *This is my business; how can you not have an answer to these questions!?*

In the end, I heard really wonderful answers from my kids, but it had to be in their own way, on their own timeline. I'm sharing this story because filling out this journal with your kids (or having them do it on their own if they're old enough) may not always be easy. It's ok to step away and come back to it when everyone's ready. Just don't give up! Building lifelong, life-changing habits takes time, and, while it might not always go as planned, it's too important to quit! Habitual gratitude helps us see the gifts in our lives and joyfully connects us with others.

Cultivating positive emotions not only feels good, but it also helps us develop enduring skills and resources that last far longer than those fleeting emotions. Trust me, these are gifts you want your children to have early in their lives and carry into adulthood.

As they grow, the ability to practice gratitude will help your children be more resilient as well as see the big picture more easily. Essentially, being able to recognize what they're grateful for will help them pursue what they want more readily and be less discouraged by setbacks. It will also enable them to find the good in day-to-day moments that crowd out the noise, discouragement, and fear that so often fills our brains.

Journey to Gratitude

My journey towards gratitude has been a slow incline. It started as a desperate measure to get out of "stuck" and to stop making fear-based decisions. I embraced a simple gratitude practice that, at the time, I wasn't even sure would work.

I was living in a very unhappy place with a failing marriage and feeling as low as a person could possibly feel. I had completely lost myself. At some point, I realized that staying in that unhappy space was an unintentional declaration that I deserved to be miserable, punished, and sad. Who knows, maybe that's what I thought I deserved at the time?

One morning at the breakfast table, I looked at each of my daughter's little faces. I pictured their lives as adults. What would life hold for them? Then I thought about what I *wanted* for them and I imagined what I would say to them, if they were in the situation I was in: denying my true self, hiding from the world, and stuck in an unhappy, unfulfilling life.

At that very moment, I knew I *wanted* to create a change. I didn't deserve to be miserable, punished, and sad. Something had to change because I *knew* this couldn't be the legacy I left my daughters. If I wanted *more* for them, I had *to be* more — for all of us. It was time to show my girls that we can face challenges head-on. That we *can* do hard things and, in fact, we *are* doing them. Every. Single. Day. I knew it was important to model courageous and brave choices. And I was ready.

This decision started me on a truly transformational journey. I learned about manifestation and mindset, and, most importantly, I uncovered and embraced the power of acknowledging and expressing gratitude. This shift became the foundation for living a more fulfilling life and opened the door for more blessings than I ever could have imagined.

What is Gratitude?

Gratitude is a true celebration of the present: a reminder to participate fully in our lives in every possible way. It's about being aware of all that surrounds you and recognizing the gifts, large and small, even in times of difficulty. This small shift in perception can take you from a scarcity mindset (there's never enough) to one of abundance (there is always more to be had). This opens your heart, mind, and soul to even greater gifts.

Providing an avenue for acknowledging the goodness in our lives, gratitude keeps us active in the present moment. It's the process of noticing goodness and expressing our appreciation. *From this, we gain a deeper understanding that the source of happiness comes from within.*

Gratitude also helps us connect to something bigger than ourselves. By acknowledging gratitude we must admit there is goodness in the world. We confront the reality that we are surrounded by gifts, both tangible and intangible.

Finally, gratitude connects us to people and things in our lives that we might otherwise take for granted. Being grateful reminds us that we are not on this journey alone. Feeling more connected leads to feeling more loved and experiencing a greater sense of self-worth.

It's also important to note that being grateful, knowing you're surrounded by blessings, and believing that your life is abundant *does not mean you don't want more or have big dreams!* When interviewing many of the kids quoted in this book I often heard "being happy with what you have and not wanting more." And, yes, that's partially true. By experiencing gratitude you will learn to recognize the joy of what you already have. Often, you'll even discover you have *way more* to be grateful for than you originally thought. But it doesn't mean there aren't big, wonderful things on the horizon, and it doesn't mean you should not dream big or want "more." Never. Ever. Settle!

I'd even go so far as to say that building a strong gratitude practice opens you up for so many more blessings and gifts. What you focus on grows — both the negative and the positive — so choose wisely, my friends. And let's teach our children to do the same.

The Science Behind Gratitude

As I began to learn more about the science behind gratitude, I dug deeper into the study of Positive Psychology[1]. I was thrilled to learn more about the *real* science behind the power of positive thinking, of which acknowledging and expressing gratitude plays a major role.

Psychologist Robert Emmons[2] teaches us that expressing gratitude has physiological effects on our brains—improving mental, physical, and relational well-being while reducing stress, resentment, and envy. What an extraordinary truth! Being grateful has a long-lasting impact on our overall experience of happiness.

> *"The more gratitude practice you perform in daily life, the deeper the benefits go and then the more profound and life-altering the benefits truly are."*
>
> **- Carla Moore**

As I began to deepen my gratitude practice, I soon discovered that when I paid attention to the positive things happening in my life, more of them appeared. I began to feel lighter and more connected with the people and things around me, and more connected to myself.

According to Psychology Today, neurologists have proven that fear and gratitude cannot reside in the brain at the same time[3]. In fact, they are completely mutually exclusive. Focusing on gratitude crowds out fear. Gratitude is the purest form of self-love: demanding nothing, costing nothing, and giving everything.

Moreso, according to the Authentic Happiness Index[4], writing down 3 good things that happen, each night before bed, has been scientifically shown to markedly increase happiness. In fact, the longer you do it, the more happiness you experience. These are hard facts, proven by science. By utilizing this gratitude journal, your children will increase their happiness, and happiness shared is joy returned!

Gratitude and Connection

As parents, we want to save our children from the type of pain and suffering we went through. We want to protect them. Have them learn by osmosis perhaps? If only that were possible!

Since we can't foresee the future and protect our children like a character out of a Marvel movie, the best we can hope to do is provide them with the right tools and resources to make the best decisions possible and know how to get themselves out of difficult situations. Trust me, they have a much better chance of doing this if they know they're not alone on the journey.

In re-building my life the way I wanted it to be, and in becoming the person I wanted my girls to look up to, I learned many lessons, most notably the power of asking for help and the importance of building a support system. To be successful in rebuilding my life, I couldn't do it alone. As it turns out, this is one of the biggest and best life lessons I've ever experienced, and it's true of all people. To be successful in *life* you cannot do it alone. We are not creatures built to do it alone. We need a support system, encouragement, and, above all else, love.

By teaching your children about gratitude and learning the impact of living gratefully together, you're showing up. You're reminding them that they *are not* alone in the world, not even when it comes to seeing beauty. It helps them build resilience and confidence in asking for support.

By simply *asking* for this support and then receiving it, I instantly felt more loved and supported — an extraordinary feeling that brought me to a new level of gratitude. A rush of emotion overcame me: I was loved and valued and worthy.

Just the other day my 15-year-old sent me a message that said "Would it be possible to go out for a little bit after school, just you and me? I miss you and I need a break." Trust me, this made it onto my personal gratitude list that night. And, of course, we did go out for a little Momma-Daughter date. But what I was so impressed with was my daughter's ability to recognize she needed support — and the safety she felt in asking for it.

When we take the time to notice and acknowledge the gifts that are already present in our lives, we learn to utilize, honor, and lean into them. I can think of no greater gift than that.

Through my personal journey and gratitude practice, I've learned that while, in theory, we should not need outside elements to prove we are loved, valued, and worthy, we're human beings and, therefore, need validation. By realizing this fact, acknowledging it, and expressing gratitude to myself and those who supported me, my relationships grew ever more deep and powerful.

Why Practice Gratitude?

"We start out knowing magic. We have shooting stars, Cosmic universes, whirlwinds inside of us. But then it gets educated away; it gets sent to sit in the corner with the gerbil cage."

- Pam Grout

One thing that was glaringly apparent during the research phase of this book is that most kids think of gratitude and gratefulness in terms of someone giving them a gift, doing a nice thing, or saying "thank you." Those are, of course, wonderful reasons to be grateful, but the real gift is discovering the billions of things that surround us at any given moment. Let's call them *small blessings*. These small blessings go unnoticed and unappreciated by most people, the majority of the time. Go ahead and give it a try — stop right now and look around you. Now list out 10 things at this exact moment you're grateful for. See? I told you we were surrounded by goodness and beauty.

The world can be a big, scary place sometimes but slowing down enough to see all that's good in your life allows for a new richness to exist. When we honor and celebrate these gifts, we start to find them in more places, more often. They literally begin to double and triple right in front of our eyes— we simply have to be awake enough to recognize them.

The famous psychologist, Carl Jung, once said: "What we resist not only persists but will grow in size." So what does that actually mean, especially to kids? Let me give an example: when my oldest daughter was two-years-old, she decided naps were no good, and she wasn't interested in taking them anymore. I was, however, not ok with this decision. I counted on nap time to get work done around the house and in my business. I needed her to nap so I could take a breath and relax for a minute. Being a momma is hard work! So I refused to allow her to skip naps. What do you imagine ensued next? Tantrums. Yup, you've got it. My strong-willed, amazing two-year-old was *finished taking naps*, so for the next several months she pitched the most awful fits, screaming, fighting, and refusing to even stay in her room for rest time (which would have been ok with me!). And I played right along; I resisted her desire to skip naps because *I needed her to nap!*

Then one day I realized this exchange was nuts, and I was nuts for participating in it. She didn't want to nap anymore, and because of my inability to accept it (and instead find other, relaxing activities for those few hours), we both felt awful and exhausted.

By resisting her request to skip nap, I invited so much more trouble into our lives. It was not my finest parenting moment, to say the least.

Looking back on it now, I realize I could have avoided the whole nasty mess by listening to my kid's request and altering my expectations. By welcoming the change, I made our lives happier and our afternoons smoother.

Rather than resisting the goodness and beauty around, that sometimes might be disguised as challenges, I encourage you to welcome them. Acknowledge them and invite them in for tea. Writing in this journal every day is taking the time to thank your gifts for existing and enriching your lives. And the hidden bonus is that, by doing so, you welcome more gifts to present themselves.

Life, as complex as it is, will always include pain and challenges. However, when you ground your thoughts and actions in gratitude, you can find beauty and joy in every aspect of life.

By actively working to focus your thoughts and center them around what you have to be grateful for, you will move away from what is lacking in your life and wrap yourself in the abundance that already exists.

Rather than resisting, try attracting!

What We Want to Attract

"To me, gratitude is taking time to be appreciative of the things you have instead of using up time to wish for things you don't have."

- Olivia, age 15

Many of you may be familiar with The Law Of Attraction, a thought practice that was taught by Buddha hundreds of years ago. At its core, the idea is that *what you have become is what you have thought.* In other words, thoughts become things, and our perception creates our reality[5].

In simple terms, the Law of Attraction is the ability to attract into our lives that which we focus on. The mind has the power to translate our thoughts and materialize them into reality. What you think will eventually become your reality. Martin Seligman, the father of Positive Psychology, believed this to be true and then went on to scientifically prove it!

If you focus on negative thoughts and emotions, those will appear in abundance. If you focus on gratitude, you will have much more to be grateful for. This thought process opens up space to achieve your goals with massive action.

Recording experiences for which we are grateful has wide-reaching positive effects including greater alertness, more energy, and increased enthusiasm, as well as a rise in determination and attentiveness. It even — and this is no joke — has been proven to reduce depression, anxiety, and risks of heart failure[6]!

Expressing Gratitude

"Gratitude is being glad about something. It is the feeling of eating ice cream. I like to say thank you for being nice. I also like to give someone a hug when I feel grateful."

- Jameson, age 6

In my house gratitude is often a big, boisterous thing. Most days you'll find me moving through the house shouting that I'm grateful for something. Just last week I walked to the mailbox, thinking to myself, *I really hope there is money in the mail!*, even though I wasn't expecting anything. Well, guess what, there **was** money in the mail. A check for $42! I started jumping and dancing around and hugging the kids shouting, "There *was* actually money in the mail!"

But that's not the only way we express gratitude. Often, when things are quiet, and I snuggle up to one of my kiddos, I'll say, "I am so grateful I get to snuggle you. I love being your momma." That's typically (although not always with the teenagers) greeted with a smile and a deeper snuggle.

I find so much joy in expressing and sharing my gratitude with and towards others. My family and I have a ritual each night during dinner. We go around the table and share our favorite parts of the day and what we're most grateful for that specific day.

Some days these things come to us easily and some days we struggle. What I especially love about this exercise is that my children are able to see that even on the most difficult of days, there's something to celebrate and something for which we can be grateful.

I also make every effort to share, on the spot, my gratitude for another person. I know firsthand the warmth and connection that verbal appreciation or affirmation can bring, not to mention the validation of feeling noticed that all human beings crave.

With that in mind, I'd like to thank the many parents who had conversations about gratitude with their kids to help me gather quotes for this book. I love the image of these conversations happening all over the world, lighting up little minds, and connecting them with the gifts of gratitude. It looks like a cell phone commercial in my head. Ahh! Connection.

I'm also unbelievably grateful to you for purchasing this journal and committing to having these life-altering and impactful conversations with your kids. I encourage you to express your gratitude in bold and brave ways. In so doing, you'll retrain your brain to see the wonder and possibility that is constantly ahead of you.

I hope you'll take these lessons into every element of your life and ignite a gratitude fire in everyone around you. The more people who develop passionate gratitude practices, the more beautiful our world will be.

Heather

CITATIONS

[1] *Positive Psychology is the scientific study of the strengths that enable individuals and communities to thrive. The field is founded on the belief that people want to lead meaningful and fulfilling lives, to cultivate what is best within themselves, and to enhance their experiences of love, work, and play.*

[2] *Robert Emmons, Ph. D., is a Professor of Psychology at the University of California at Davis. His research is in the field of personality psychology, emotion psychology, and psychology of religion.*

[3] *Korb, Alex, Ph.D. (2012, Nov) The Grateful Brain. retrieved from https://www.psychologytoday.com/us/blog/prefrontal-nudity/201211/the-grateful-brain.*

[4] *Dr. Martin E. P. Seligman is known as the "founder" of positive psychology. Learn more about quiz yourself at https://www.authentichappiness.sas.upenn.edu/*

[5] *For more about The Law of Attraction, I recommend starting at TheLawofAttraction.com.*

[6] *Read Dr. Martian E.P. Seligman's findings on positive health https://positivehealthresearch.org/team/Seligman*

WAYS TO USE THIS
Journal

"The feeling of gratitude is a big hug. I am grateful a lot but I don't always take it into consideration. The thoughts of gratitude get lost in my mind like a penny in a jar of quarters. I'm always grateful for something — I just don't always realize it right away."

TESSA, AGE 9

This journal contains room for 180 separate entries. I invite and encourage you and your kids to write in it however often you want. Some people practice gratitude as a daily ritual, some journal a few times a week, and others weekly. There is no right or wrong way to record your gratitude. Trust your gut.

Remember, no child is too young to participate in these conversations. Children who can't write yet can dictate their responses to you or even draw a picture that shows what they're grateful for.

You'll also find 180 unique prompts included in this journal. Each prompt is designed to help everyone think creatively about life and all that you have to be grateful for. Enjoy exploring areas you may never have even considered, such as being grateful for something in the past, and then watch in wonder as the beauty continues to grow, right before your very eyes!

When sitting down to record gratitude, you may want to encourage kids to reflect on these things:

- A person that has impacted them that day

- A thought that resonates with them

- An action they or someone else took

- An act of joy they have experienced or provided

Journaling is not the only way to connect with gratitude. I personally bring gratitude into my life in a multitude of ways. Here are a few suggestions. Consider adding some of these to your gratitude practices and do what feels right!

- Breathe deeply before and after your gratitude journaling. This ensures you're present, grounded, and mindful.

- Create art! There are many different ways to express your feelings, thanks, and gratitude through creative expression.

- Mentally acknowledge things you're grateful for at the moment when the thought first occurs to you.

- Redirect anger or frustration by finding something to be grateful for, even in a frustrating moment. For example, when your children refuse to put their shoes on so you can leave the house! When I find myself in that situation (which happens daily), I try to express gratitude for us having shoes to wear. I will literally stop what I'm doing, count to 10, and list out 5 things I'm grateful in that very moment; and, hopefully, when I open my eyes, the shoes will be on!

- Express thanks, often, and to everyone you encounter!

- Write a letter of thanks to someone who has made a difference in your life.

- Stop someone throughout your day, and offer a compliment.

- Have a shared family (or friend) gratitude practice.

- Go deep with your gratitude. Rather than rattling off a quick list of things, elaborate about what you are grateful for and why.

- Make it personal — focus on the people that impact your life. It will help you connect with those people on many levels.

- Find gratitude for little things that will help you reach big goals. Envision yourself having accomplished those goals.

One Final Thought

I've mentioned several times that I asked parents to have conversations with their kids about gratitude so that I could better understand what kids knew about the overall concept of gratitude and also gather the quotes you'll see throughout the book.

Invariably, with each request, I would get a response from the parents that said something like "Wow. This was harder than I expected it to be, but it led to a great conversation." I wasn't at all surprised by this because developing a deep understanding of what gratitude is, how it feels to be grateful, and what it feels like when someone shares gratitude with you, is a big-time undertaking. I'd even venture to say it's a life-long undertaking that we never fully master, but it's always helping us grow into happier, more thoughtful, and grateful humans.

Imagine, if you will, a generation of adults who have been taught to experience gratitude and gratefulness in their ordinary lives. An entire generation of adults that take the time to notice the beauty and gifts that are naturally there, even when things are difficult. Can you envision a generation of adults that freely and joyfully express their gratitude for others? Imagine how this would impact world views, communities, families, and overall happiness. This is what I call on you to help build—a more grateful and connected world. We can start today!

Let me share one final story with you. This is the story of seven-year-old Jasmine. I asked Jasmine's mom to chat with her about gratitude and share the conversation with me as part of my research. Keep your eyes open for Jasmine's quote as you work your way through the journal. Miranda, Jasmine's mom, told me they had a lovely chat, and it seemed Jasmine was really engaged in the discussion. After the conversation, unbeknownst to her parents, Jasmine wrote a letter of gratitude for her parents and brother. Her mom said, "she just quietly worked on this by herself with no prompting." I was so touched when she shared the letter with me and simply had to share it with you.

Here is Jasmine's letter:

"I love my mom for helping me every day. She helps me do things. I also love my dad. He makes us dinner every day. So please respect your parents for helping you every day, and you can help your parents do everyday things. I love you Amani. I love you Dad. I love you Mom."

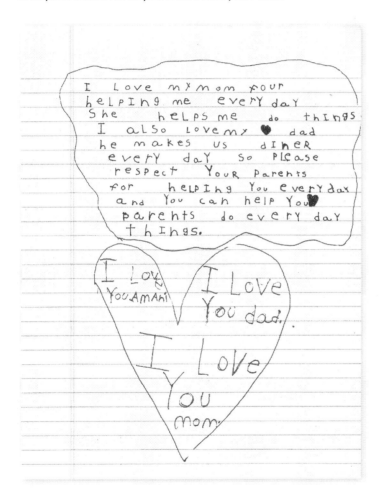

These conversations lead to deep thinking for both children and adults. They lead to all of us being more attentive and thoughtful and living in the moment. Writing in this journal and developing a gratitude practice is a gift you give yourself and your family.

START
Today

"Gratitude means more than thank you. When you're really grateful for something, it's like a blessing carries you."

MADELINE, AGE 13

Today I am grateful for...

- *Playing outside. We played freeze tag and it was a lot of fun!*
- *Chocolate ice cream*
- *Reading books at bedtime with my family*

What went well today, and why?

- *I felt really great when I stuck up for myself at recess. It was hard to do but I did it anyway and I was proud.*
- *We were on time for school because I was helpful and got ready right away*
- *I finished the book I've been reading. I set aside specific time to read for the last week and it paid off!*

How did you express your gratitude today?

I said thank you and gave a smile when my friend held the door open for me at school.

What item of clothing are you most grateful for today?

It was really cold today so I am grateful for my hat and gloves. I was happy to be warm!

Sample Journal Entry

Today I am grateful for...

What went well today, and why?

How did you express your gratitude today?

What is the prettiest thing you saw today?

Today I am grateful for...

What went well today, and why?

How did you express your gratitude today?

What sound do you love to hear?

Today I am grateful for...

What went well today, and why?

How did you express your gratitude today?

Which body part are you most grateful for today?

Today I am grateful for...

What went well today, and why?

How did you express your gratitude today?

What memory makes you smile?

Today I am grateful for...

What went well today, and why?

How did you express your gratitude today?

What food are you most grateful for?

"I like to show gratitude by being helpful and doing something kind. When someone is thankful for me, I feel even more thankful."

ELIAS, AGE 9

Today I am grateful for...

What went well today, and why?

How did you express your gratitude today?

What game are you grateful for today?

Today I am grateful for...

What went well today, and why?

How did you express your gratitude today?

What unusual thing are you grateful for?

Today I am grateful for...

What went well today, and why?

How did you express your gratitude today?

What surprised you, in a good way, today?

Today I am grateful for...

What went well today, and why?

How did you express your gratitude today?

What do you most enjoy about taking a walk?

Today I am grateful for...

What went well today, and why?

How did you express your gratitude today?

Which adult was helpful to you today?

Today I am grateful for...

What went well today, and why?

How did you express your gratitude today?

What room in your house are you most grateful for?

"Being grateful means loving something."

JOHNNY, AGE 4

Today I am grateful for...

What went well today, and why?

How did you express your gratitude today?

What is the yummiest thing you ate today?

Today I am grateful for...

What went well today, and why?

How did you express your gratitude today?

What made you the happiest today?

Today I am grateful for...

What went well today, and why?

How did you express your gratitude today?

What chores are you grateful for?

Today I am grateful for...

What went well today, and why?

How did you express your gratitude today?

What are you looking forward to?

Today I am grateful for...

What went well today, and why?

How did you express your gratitude today?

Which person are you most grateful for today?

"To me, gratitude means recognizing what someone has done for you and trying to either pay it back or pay it forward, however you can. It's reflecting that which has been shown to you."

LINCOLN, AGE 19

Today I am grateful for...

What went well today, and why?

How did you express your gratitude today?

What did you enjoy learning today?

Today I am grateful for...

What went well today, and why?

How did you express your gratitude today?

What made you laugh today?

Today I am grateful for...

What went well today, and why?

How did you express your gratitude today?

What made you joyful today?

Today I am grateful for...

What went well today, and why?

How did you express your gratitude today?

What made you hopeful today?

Today I am grateful for...

What went well today, and why?

How did you express your gratitude today?

How were you courageous today?

Today I am grateful for...

What went well today, and why?

How did you express your gratitude today?

What silliness made you happy today?

"Being grateful is when you thank someone. It makes me happy."

KENNA, AGE 6

Today I am grateful for...

What went well today, and why?

How did you express your gratitude today?

How did you help another person today?

Today I am grateful for...

What went well today, and why?

How did you express your gratitude today?

What kindness are you grateful for today?

Today I am grateful for...

What went well today, and why?

How did you express your gratitude today?

What sweet, simple thing are you grateful for today?

Today I am grateful for...

What went well today, and why?

How did you express your gratitude today?

What brave thing did you do today?

Today I am grateful for...

What went well today, and why?

How did you express your gratitude today?

What do you enjoy most about your family?

"When someone asks me to play with them I feel happy, grateful, and not alone. I say yes, and am kind to them to show them gratitude and kindness."

PATRICK, AGE 8

Today I am grateful for...

What went well today, and why?

How did you express your gratitude today?

What is your favorite treat?

Today I am grateful for...

What went well today, and why?

How did you express your gratitude today?

What kindness did you show another person today?

Today I am grateful for...

What went well today, and why?

How did you express your gratitude today?

What is the funniest thing you experienced today?

Today I am grateful for...

What went well today, and why?

How did you express your gratitude today?

What positive lesson did you learn today?

Today I am grateful for...

What went well today, and why?

How did you express your gratitude today?

What are you most excited about today?

Today I am grateful for...

What went well today, and why?

How did you express your gratitude today?

What new thing are you excited to try?

"Gratitude is loving, kindness, gentleness, and showing respect."

KAILEA, AGE 9

Today I am grateful for...

What went well today, and why?

How did you express your gratitude today?

What made you feel like you did a good job today?

Today I am grateful for...

What went well today, and why?

How did you express your gratitude today?

What is your favorite song?

Today I am grateful for...

What went well today, and why?

How did you express your gratitude today?

What physical activity did you most enjoy today?

TODAY'S DATE _____ / _____ / _____

Today I am grateful for...

What went well today, and why?

How did you express your gratitude today?

What were you excited about today?

Today I am grateful for...

What went well today, and why?

How did you express your gratitude today?

What family member are you most grateful for today?

"I think gratitude is accepting anything that is given to you and being happy in your heart about it, even if you don't like the gift."

JACK, AGE 10

Today I am grateful for...

What went well today, and why?

How did you express your gratitude today?

How did you make yourself proud today?

Today I am grateful for...

What went well today, and why?

How did you express your gratitude today?

What strange thing did you enjoy today?

Today I am grateful for...

What went well today, and why?

How did you express your gratitude today?

What is your favorite season?

Today I am grateful for...

What went well today, and why?

How did you express your gratitude today?

What are you most grateful for in the Fall?

Today I am grateful for...

What went well today, and why?

How did you express your gratitude today?

What Holiday are you most grateful for?

Today I am grateful for...

What went well today, and why?

How did you express your gratitude today?

What did you create today?

"Gratitude is being very, very kind."

DIGBY, AGE 7

Today I am grateful for...

What went well today, and why?

How did you express your gratitude today?

What are you most grateful for about your age?

Today I am grateful for...

What went well today, and why?

How did you express your gratitude today?

What fear have you overcome?

Today I am grateful for...

What went well today, and why?

How did you express your gratitude today?

What made you jump for joy today?

Today I am grateful for...

What went well today, and why?

How did you express your gratitude today?

What boring task do you enjoy?

Today I am grateful for...

What went well today, and why?

How did you express your gratitude today?

What item of clothing are you most grateful for today?

"I think gratitude is when you feel genuinely thankful for something, and I'm grateful for my family."

EVE, AGE 13

Today I am grateful for...

What went well today, and why?

How did you express your gratitude today?

What daily activity brought you joy today?

Today I am grateful for...

What went well today, and why?

How did you express your gratitude today?

What new thing did you learn today?

Today I am grateful for...

What went well today, and why?

How did you express your gratitude today?

What did you most enjoy doing alone today?

Today I am grateful for...

What went well today, and why?

How did you express your gratitude today?

What did you enjoy doing with a friend today?

Today I am grateful for...

What went well today, and why?

How did you express your gratitude today?

What are you most grateful for in the Spring?

Today I am grateful for...

What went well today, and why?

How did you express your gratitude today?

Which holiday food are you most grateful for?

"Being grateful means saying thank you and giving something back."

MELANIE, AGE 8

Today I am grateful for...

What went well today, and why?

How did you express your gratitude today?

What is your favorite ice cream flavor?

Today I am grateful for...

What went well today, and why?

How did you express your gratitude today?

Share a memory that makes you happy.

Today I am grateful for...

What went well today, and why?

How did you express your gratitude today?

What quiet pleasure are you most grateful for today?

Today I am grateful for...

What went well today, and why?

How did you express your gratitude today?

How did you take care of your body today?

Today I am grateful for...

What went well today, and why?

How did you express your gratitude today?

What are you hopeful about?

"Gratitude means a sense of fulfillment to someone; not like I owe them (I might) but I am lucky to have them, and I am happy they helped me through a tough situation anywhere in life."

RYLAN, AGE 13

Today I am grateful for...

What went well today, and why?

How did you express your gratitude today?

What are you super excited about?

Today I am grateful for...

What went well today, and why?

How did you express your gratitude today?

What movie could you watch over and over again?

Today I am grateful for...

What went well today, and why?

How did you express your gratitude today?

What is your theme song?

Today I am grateful for...

What went well today, and why?

How did you express your gratitude today?

Who was your biggest fan today?

Today I am grateful for...

What went well today, and why?

How did you express your gratitude today?

Which holiday tradition do you most enjoy?

Today I am grateful for...

What went well today, and why?

How did you express your gratitude today?

What drink do you most enjoy?

"I'm always grateful
when my family
is together."

SCARLETT, AGE 6

Today I am grateful for...

What went well today, and why?

How did you express your gratitude today?

What seemingly "usual" thing are you most grateful for?

Today I am grateful for...

What went well today, and why?

How did you express your gratitude today?

What are you most grateful for in the Winter?

Today I am grateful for...

What went well today, and why?

How did you express your gratitude today?

What about your current surroundings are you most grateful for?

Today I am grateful for...

What went well today, and why?

How did you express your gratitude today?

What modern invention are you most grateful for?

Today I am grateful for...

What went well today, and why?

How did you express your gratitude today?

What dessert are you most grateful for?

"Gratitude is being so kind and playing nicely."

AMELIA, AGE 3

Today I am grateful for...

What went well today, and why?

How did you express your gratitude today?

What memory makes you laugh until your side hurts?

Today I am grateful for...

What went well today, and why?

How did you express your gratitude today?

What memory most warms your heart?

Today I am grateful for...

What went well today, and why?

How did you express your gratitude today?

What mess are you grateful for?

Today I am grateful for...

What went well today, and why?

How did you express your gratitude today?

What conversation are you grateful for today?

Today I am grateful for...

What went well today, and why?

How did you express your gratitude today?

What piece of advice are you most grateful for today?

Today I am grateful for...

What went well today, and why?

How did you express your gratitude today?

What is the strangest thing you are grateful for today?

"Gratitude is not just being thankful inside but being thankful enough to share with others."

NORA, AGE 15

Today I am grateful for...

What went well today, and why?

How did you express your gratitude today?

Who did you help today?

Today I am grateful for...

What went well today, and why?

How did you express your gratitude today?

What did you do today that made you proud?

Today I am grateful for...

What went well today, and why?

How did you express your gratitude today?

Name one place you are grateful for having visited.

Today I am grateful for...

What went well today, and why?

How did you express your gratitude today?

How did you show kindness today?

Today I am grateful for...

What went well today, and why?

How did you express your gratitude today?

**What is one thing that didn't turn out the way you wanted
but turned out to be a good thing?**

"Being grateful makes me feel good because sometimes it means giving hugs."

OLIVIA, AGE 5

Today I am grateful for...

What went well today, and why?

How did you express your gratitude today?

What toy are you most grateful for?

Today I am grateful for...

What went well today, and why?

How did you express your gratitude today?

What learning opportunity are you most grateful for today?

Today I am grateful for...

What went well today, and why?

How did you express your gratitude today?

What are you grateful for that's "old"?

Today I am grateful for...

What went well today, and why?

How did you express your gratitude today?

What change are you most grateful for?

Today I am grateful for...

What went well today, and why?

How did you express your gratitude today?

What makes you feel lucky?

Today I am grateful for...

What went well today, and why?

How did you express your gratitude today?

What act of love are you most grateful for today?

"I'm grateful for a lot of things but gratitude, to me, is expressing thankfulness for something or someone."

RYANN, AGE 11

Today I am grateful for...

What went well today, and why?

How did you express your gratitude today?

What seemingly silly thing are you grateful for today?

Today I am grateful for...

What went well today, and why?

How did you express your gratitude today?

What flowers make you feel joyful?

Today I am grateful for...

What went well today, and why?

How did you express your gratitude today?

What new idea are you grateful for?

Today I am grateful for...

What went well today, and why?

How did you express your gratitude today?

What compromise are you grateful for today?

Today I am grateful for...

What went well today, and why?

How did you express your gratitude today?

What are you most grateful for giving today?

"I think being grateful means you do something nice for someone."

BENJAMIN, AGE 4

Today I am grateful for...

What went well today, and why?

How did you express your gratitude today?

What are you most grateful for in the Summer?

Today I am grateful for...

What went well today, and why?

How did you express your gratitude today?

What made you cheerful today?

Today I am grateful for...

What went well today, and why?

How did you express your gratitude today?

How did your family make you happy today?

Today I am grateful for...

What went well today, and why?

How did you express your gratitude today?

How did you experience joy today?

Today I am grateful for...

What went well today, and why?

How did you express your gratitude today?

What dreams do you have for when you are an adult?

Today I am grateful for...

What went well today, and why?

How did you express your gratitude today?

What do you take pleasure in that most people might not?

"When someone helps me I'm grateful and I thank them. They feel good about themselves, so we both get repaid for it. I'm grateful for the loyalty and support of my friends."

CHARLIE, AGE 15

Today I am grateful for...

What went well today, and why?

How did you express your gratitude today?

What is one little thing you enjoyed that turned out to be a big thing?

Today I am grateful for...

What went well today, and why?

How did you express your gratitude today?

What "unimportant" thing are you most grateful for today?

Today I am grateful for...

What went well today, and why?

How did you express your gratitude today?

How did you change your mind today?

Today I am grateful for...

What went well today, and why?

How did you express your gratitude today?

What indulgence are you most grateful for?

Today I am grateful for...

What went well today, and why?

How did you express your gratitude today?

How did you serve others today?

"Gratitude is saying thank you or I'm sorry. It's being nice. When someone shows me gratitude I feel good because it means I did a nice thing for them."

CYRUS, AGE 5

Today I am grateful for...

What went well today, and why?

How did you express your gratitude today?

How did you play today?

Today I am grateful for...

What went well today, and why?

How did you express your gratitude today?

What friend are you most grateful for today?

Today I am grateful for...

What went well today, and why?

How did you express your gratitude today?

What excites you about getting older?

Today I am grateful for...

What went well today, and why?

How did you express your gratitude today?

What random act of kindness did you experience today?

Today I am grateful for...

What went well today, and why?

How did you express your gratitude today?

What did you let go of today?

Today I am grateful for...

What went well today, and why?

How did you express your gratitude today?

Who did you forgive today?

"Being thankful for something someone did and showing it to them with your words and actions."

SIMON, AGE 12

Today I am grateful for...

What went well today, and why?

How did you express your gratitude today?

What soothed you today?

Today I am grateful for...

What went well today, and why?

How did you express your gratitude today?

How did "work" become play today?

Today I am grateful for...

What went well today, and why?

How did you express your gratitude today?

How did someone come through for you today?

Today I am grateful for...

What went well today, and why?

How did you express your gratitude today?

What delighted you today?

Today I am grateful for...

What went well today, and why?

How did you express your gratitude today?

What made you feel connected today?

\

"Gratitude is when you are happy. It's when someone gives you something and you give them a hug or smile back."

ISHAAN, AGE 6

Today I am grateful for...

What went well today, and why?

How did you express your gratitude today?

What new thing did you experience today?

Today I am grateful for...

What went well today, and why?

How did you express your gratitude today?

What surprise are you grateful for?

Today I am grateful for...

What went well today, and why?

How did you express your gratitude today?

What is your favorite way to comfort yourself?

Today I am grateful for...

What went well today, and why?

How did you express your gratitude today?

What do you enjoy most about going for a walk?

Today I am grateful for...

What went well today, and why?

How did you express your gratitude today?

How did you make someone else's day better?

Today I am grateful for...

What went well today, and why?

How did you express your gratitude today?

What do you love most about clouds?

"Gratitude means being thankful for the things and people you have. I'm thankful for being on this earth and having a healthy heart, my house, my bed, and my toys. Oh yeah, and my family! Gratitude feels like being really happy inside."

HENRY, AGE 7

Today I am grateful for...

What went well today, and why?

How did you express your gratitude today?

Where is your happy place?

Today I am grateful for...

What went well today, and why?

How did you express your gratitude today?

What did you read today that you are grateful for?

Today I am grateful for...

What went well today, and why?

How did you express your gratitude today?

What is something invisible you are grateful for?

Today I am grateful for...

What went well today, and why?

How did you express your gratitude today?

What sound made you smile today?

Today I am grateful for...

What went well today, and why?

How did you express your gratitude today?

What smell made you happy today?

"Gratitude can be simple. I'm grateful I can walk, talk and breathe. I'm grateful my body functions. I'm grateful for the opportunities I have. Gratitude is about being ok with what you have without wishing for more."

ZOE, AGE 17

Today I am grateful for...

What went well today, and why?

How did you express your gratitude today?

What animal are you most grateful for today?

Today I am grateful for...

What went well today, and why?

How did you express your gratitude today?

What did you do to make your family or community better today?

Today I am grateful for...

What went well today, and why?

How did you express your gratitude today?

How does it make you feel to spend time with friends?

Today I am grateful for...

What went well today, and why?

How did you express your gratitude today?

What lesson in school are you most grateful for?

Today I am grateful for...

What went well today, and why?

How did you express your gratitude today?

What sound most comforts you?

Today I am grateful for...

What went well today, and why?

How did you express your gratitude today?

What friendship are you most grateful for?

"Gratitude is a feeling of being thankful. I show I'm grateful with my kind words. I feel grateful for people who take care of me, in my family and in society. I feel grateful for people who are trying to make the world better."

ALIDA, AGE 8

Today I am grateful for...

What went well today, and why?

How did you express your gratitude today?

What's your favorite thing to do in the summer?

Today I am grateful for...

What went well today, and why?

How did you express your gratitude today?

Who do you love to see smile?

Today I am grateful for...

What went well today, and why?

How did you express your gratitude today?

What makes you feel peaceful?

Today I am grateful for...

What went well today, and why?

How did you express your gratitude today?

What book are you most grateful for?

Today I am grateful for...

What went well today, and why?

How did you express your gratitude today?

What outdoor activity are you most grateful for?

"To be grateful is to be appreciative. If I was grateful to my brother, I would bring him monkey – which is his cuddle toy since he was a baby."

ANNEMARIE, AGE 7

Today I am grateful for...

What went well today, and why?

How did you express your gratitude today?

What is your special gift?

Today I am grateful for...

What went well today, and why?

How did you express your gratitude today?

What is the best gift you've ever received?

Today I am grateful for...

What went well today, and why?

How did you express your gratitude today?

What's the most beautiful place you've ever visited?

Today I am grateful for...

What went well today, and why?

How did you express your gratitude today?

What do you dream of doing?

Today I am grateful for...

What went well today, and why?

How did you express your gratitude today?

Where do you want to go on a vacation?

Today I am grateful for...

What went well today, and why?

How did you express your gratitude today?

What's your favorite way to use your body?

"Gratitude is a thought about happiness. When I talk to or think about gratitude it gives me a visual memory of my day."

OLIVIER, AGE 10

Today I am grateful for...

What went well today, and why?

How did you express your gratitude today?

What is your favorite vacation memory?

Today I am grateful for...

What went well today, and why?

How did you express your gratitude today?

What makes you feel strong?

Today I am grateful for...

What went well today, and why?

How did you express your gratitude today?

Who understands you better than anyone else?

Today I am grateful for...

What went well today, and why?

How did you express your gratitude today?

Who is your favorite person to talk to?

Today I am grateful for...

What went well today, and why?

How did you express your gratitude today?

Who do you know supports you no matter what?

"Being grateful means you care about other people. Gratitude means you feel happy."

ISAIAH, AGE 6

Today I am grateful for...

What went well today, and why?

How did you express your gratitude today?

Who makes you feel loved?

Today I am grateful for...

What went well today, and why?

How did you express your gratitude today?

What made you feel grown-up?

Today I am grateful for...

What went well today, and why?

How did you express your gratitude today?

What do you love about yourself?

Today I am grateful for...

What went well today, and why?

How did you express your gratitude today?

Who would you like to thank today?

Today I am grateful for...

What went well today, and why?

How did you express your gratitude today?

Whose life did you make a difference in today?

Today I am grateful for...

What went well today, and why?

How did you express your gratitude today?

Who made a big difference in your life today?

"When I'm grateful I feel I'm really happy because something good happened to me, and I'm having a really good time."

PHILIP, AGE 9

Today I am grateful for...

What went well today, and why?

How did you express your gratitude today?

What compliment did you receive today?

Today I am grateful for...

What went well today, and why?

How did you express your gratitude today?

What chaos are you grateful for today?

Today I am grateful for...

What went well today, and why?

How did you express your gratitude today?

What made you truly feel good today?

Today I am grateful for...

What went well today, and why?

How did you express your gratitude today?

Use one beautiful word to describe yourself.

Today I am grateful for...

What went well today, and why?

How did you express your gratitude today?

What small comfort did you experience today?

"Gratitude means being nice because you wanna be kind. I'm grateful for my family because we stick together and being grateful feels like a hug. My favorite way to show gratitude is with snuggles."

GRAHAM, AGE 4

Today I am grateful for...

What went well today, and why?

How did you express your gratitude today?

What did you do today that felt great?

Today I am grateful for...

What went well today, and why?

How did you express your gratitude today?

What are you curious about today?

Today I am grateful for...

What went well today, and why?

How did you express your gratitude today?

What compliment did you give today?

Today I am grateful for...

What went well today, and why?

How did you express your gratitude today?

What did you learn about yourself today?

Today I am grateful for...

What went well today, and why?

How did you express your gratitude today?

What new experience are you grateful for today?

Today I am grateful for...

What went well today, and why?

How did you express your gratitude today?

What made you feel really good today?

Today I am grateful for...

What went well today, and why?

How did you express your gratitude today?

How did you reward yourself today?

"If someone shows gratitude towards me, it makes me feel happy and it means more than you would think."

MACKENZIE, AGE 11

Today I am grateful for...

What went well today, and why?

How did you express your gratitude today?

How did you celebrate today?

Today I am grateful for...

What went well today, and why?

How did you express your gratitude today?

Who do you want to celebrate today?

Today I am grateful for...

What went well today, and why?

How did you express your gratitude today?

What was really difficult but you did it anyway?

Today I am grateful for...

What went well today, and why?

How did you express your gratitude today?

Who are you proud of today?

Today I am grateful for...

What went well today, and why?

How did you express your gratitude today?

What new thing are you excited to try?

Today I am grateful for...

What went well today, and why?

How did you express your gratitude today?

How did you make yourself happy today?

"I feel happy when someone shows me gratitude because it's friendly, and I feel thankful when someone else is grateful for me."

OLIVIA AND SOPHIA, AGE 6

Today I am grateful for...

What went well today, and why?

How did you express your gratitude today?

What did you celebrate today?

Today I am grateful for...

What went well today, and why?

How did you express your gratitude today?

Where do you like to go when you're feeling sad?

Today I am grateful for...

What went well today, and why?

How did you express your gratitude today?

Who is your favorite person to snuggle with?

Today I am grateful for...

What went well today, and why?

How did you express your gratitude today?

What mistake are you most grateful for?

Today I am grateful for...

What went well today, and why?

How did you express your gratitude today?

What challenge are you most grateful for?

Today I am grateful for...

What went well today, and why?

How did you express your gratitude today?

What do you strongly believe in?

Today I am grateful for...

What went well today, and why?

How did you express your gratitude today?

How did you make someone feel good about themselves today?

Today I am grateful for...

What went well today, and why?

How did you express your gratitude today?

What are you most grateful for that you can't hold in your hand?

About the Author

Heather Vickery is an award-winning business owner and Success Coach, with over 20 years of experience and Positive Psychology certification from the University of Pennsylvania. She leverages her entrepreneurial skills and expertise to coach individuals towards greater personal and professional fulfillment. A celebrated public speaker, Heather inspires audiences and empowers attendees with the tools they need to live bold and successful lives through creating balance with time management, as well as countless systems, strategies, and boundaries. Heather is a mom of four, dedicated community member, and a fierce advocate for social justice. She's also the executive producer and host of the Brave Files podcast.

   @vickeryandco

When you measure life in gratitude, joy and success are around every corner. - Heather Vickery

Gratitude becomes a gateway to personal and professional success.

Words of wisdom, from noted thinkers of the past and passionate entrepreneurs of today, bolster your reflections as you move through this journal.

"I write in this journal every night before bed and I love it. The prompts that change daily are everything!"

When we choose bravely, in every possible way, our lives are infinitely better.

Tune in each week for a dose of inspiration from a guest who's living courageously.

Inspiration. Motivation. Human Connection.

Find us on Apple Podcast, Spotify, Stitcher, Google and anywhere you enjoy podcasts.

Made in the USA
Las Vegas, NV
25 October 2021

33051246R00133